Chinese Water Deer

by Arnold Cooke and Lynne Farrell

CONTENTS

Chinese Water Deer
By Arnold Cooke & Lynne Farrell

Published by the Mammal Society and The British Deer Society

The Mammal Society
Registered Charity No. 278918
Registered Office:
The Mammal Society
15 Cloisters House
8 Battersea Park Road
London SW8 4BG

The British Deer Society
Registered Charity No. 228659
Registered Office:
The British Deer Society
Burgate Manor
Fordingbridge
Hampshire SP6 1EF

ISBN 0 906282 38 1

This is one of a series of booklets on deer in Britain published jointly by
The Mammal Society and The British Deer Society.

REGISTERED CHARITY NO. 278918

Drawings by Sarah Wroot.
Map produced by Henry Arnold at the Biological Records Centre, Institute of Terrestrial Ecology
Photographs on Cover, pages 1, 19, 20, 22, 23, 24, 26, 28 by Michael Clark, Tewin Orchard
Photographs on pages 4, 5, 7, 8, 9, 12, 13, 15, 29 by Arnold Cooke & Lynne Farrell

Typesetting and printing by SP Press, Wedmore Road, Cheddar, Somerset.

Introduction

The Chinese water deer *Hydropotes inermis* is believed to be the most primitive extant member of the family Cervidae, on the basis of the buck's large canine teeth and absence of antlers. Musk deer also lack antlers and have large canines, but are placed in the family Moschidae.

There are two subspecies of water deer. *Hydropotes inermis inermis* is found in parts of China and is the subspecies that has been introduced to this country. The second subspecies, *Hydropotes inermis argyropus*, is found in Korea. Little is known in the west about this subspecies, but one correspondent has informed us that its range within Korea remains reasonably extensive and the animal is plentiful.

In contrast, the Chinese subspecies has become seriously restricted in both range and numbers. It is often said that not much is known about this subspecies either, but we now have a reasonable amount of information from a variety of sources. These include recent basic ecological investigations on the surviving populations in China, two detailed postgraduate studies from Whipsnade Wild Animal Park in Bedfordshire and our own work on a population in Woodwalton Fen National Nature Reserve in Cambridgeshire, which has now been in progress for more than 20 years. While it is true to state that studies in the wild in this country are restricted, it is no longer true that little is known about the animal more generally. The account in this book is based totally on information on the Chinese subspecies. Because of the recent availability of information from China and because of the plight of the species in that country, a section about China has been included.

Appearance

Water deer stand only 50-55 centimetres at the shoulder. In China they weigh about 15 kilograms (whole body weight); in one population, for instance, males averaged 14.8 kilograms and females 15.1 kilograms. These figures are close to mean weights for feral deer from sites in Cambridgeshire: bucks 14.2 kilograms and does 15.6 kilograms. However, at Whipsnade, reported mean weights for samples of deer since the 1930s are only 11.1-11.7 kilograms for bucks and 11.7-13.4 kilograms for does. Thus the Whipsnade animals are lighter by about 20%. The biggest animals we have weighed from Cambridgeshire have been 18.5 kilograms for a male and 17.4 kilograms for a female. However, our sample sizes have been small and larger water deer undoubtedly exist. On average, female water deer have been found to be marginally heavier than males, an observation that cannot be totally explained by some of the females being pregnant. Although buck water deer are taller than bucks of Reeves' muntjac *Muntiacus reevesi*, the two are of similar weight. Comparing the does, water deer are about 30% heavier.

Doe in summer coat

Water deer much more closely resemble the elegant roe *Capreolus capreolus* than the often hunched, rather pig-like muntjac. Indeed, they are sometimes mis-reported as roe deer, as well as being often called 'muntjacs'. So how can they be distinguished from the other species? The rear views of the three species are totally different. Water deer have a barely-noticeable tail 5-10 centimetres in length, although this may stick out on bucks in the rut in mid winter. There is no white on the tail nor on the rump, but the latter can be paler than the rest of the coat. In contrast, the roe deer has a white caudal patch, while the muntjac has white under its broad tail which it often erects when alarmed.

In general appearance, their hind legs look particularly muscular and are longer than the front legs, so the hindquarters are higher than the shoulders. The ears are large, hairy and held erect. The eyes and nose can resemble three shiny black buttons, this being particularly true of bucks in their thick winter coat. Coat colour in winter is variable, with pale brown and a peppery grey-brown being common. Sometimes deer in winter coat have a silvery appearance to their backs. This is when each individual hair has become broken, but the cause of this condition remains unknown. Deer change to summer coat in the spring, usually in April and May. At this time of year bucks, especially, look scruffy with tufts of old hair hanging down and with bald patches. A few weeks later, they look sleek in their red summer coats. Transition back to winter coat occurs in the autumn.

Some individuals can be recognised with careful observation on the basis of scars on their bodies, tears in their ears and facial characteristics. Does often have white or pale bands above more pointed noses while bucks often have dark grey or black. Bucks have thicker necks.

Initially the dark brown fawns have white spots, but these disappear after two months. By late summer their coats have a soft, rather shaggy appearance and are unmarked. By the time of the rut, when they are about six months old, they are about 80% of their full weight and are usually obviously lighter in build than older deer.

When surprised on a path through dense habitat such as woodland or a reedbed, water deer will frequently turn and run off up the ride, perhaps then dodging down a side turning. In contrast, a muntjac, on finding itself similarly confronted, is likely to leap into the nearest cover. When running off, water deer often adopt a bounding gait in which the back legs are flung high into the air.

Tusks

A well known feature of the water deer is that bucks have no antlers, but instead have well developed canine teeth or tusks for fighting. The first water deer recorded in the Monks Wood area of Cambridgeshire was an adult buck. It was reported to the police as a lion and provoked considerable activity until it was hit by a motor car later that day and killed.

Bucks grazing with tusks held back

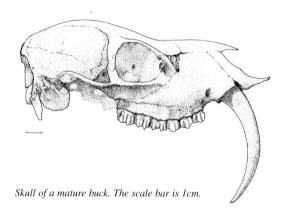

Skull of a mature buck. The scale bar is 1cm.

In young bucks, canines erupt in the autumn and by the end of winter are about half their final length. At Whipsnade, researchers have had little difficulty in seeing these short tusks on free-ranging, first winter bucks. At Woodwalton, however, cover is much denser and our views are less clear or prolonged; we are able to confirm short tusks on only about 20% of the first winter bucks. By spring, though, the developing tusks are readily apparent, enabling the sex ratio to be confirmed as roughly parity.

The tusks continue to grow and remain open-rooted until about eighteen months to two years of age. In Cambridgeshire, tusks measured on adult bucks have averaged 56 millimetres in length from the gum-line, with the longest being 72 millimetres. Mean tusk length for a sample of Whipsnade bucks, measured in the 1990s, was only 44 millimetres, significantly smaller than in Cambridgeshire. There has been a certain amount of confusion in the literature over tusk size, as there are several ways of measuring length. If root length is included, this will increase reported length by about 40%. Does have small canines that erupt during their first winter. These reach an average length of 5 millimetres for Cambridgeshire animals (maximum measured, 8 millimetres).

In bucks the tusks are fairly loose in their sockets and effectively hinged, with their position being controlled by facial muscles. They can be held back so as not to impede grazing or can be brought forwards and inwards for fighting, with the top lip taking on a snarl. This snarling action pulls forward a section of movable gum which brings the tusk into its most forward position. The loose attachment of the tusk may dampen impacts suffered when fighting. Nevertheless, broken tusks are not particularly unusual amongst older bucks. Tusks are lens-shaped in cross-section. The inner face is polished smooth by contact with the side of the lower lip. A sharp rear edge is thereby maintained, as well as a point. The tusk is used for both stabbing and tearing when fighting. Wear on its inside face can eventually expose the central cavity of the canine.

Signs

The two species whose signs might be confused with those of water deer are the roe and the muntjac. Droppings of water deer are black or dark brown. They are drawn out to a point at one end and slightly rounded at the other. Their appearance and range of sizes, 1.0-1.5 centimetres in length by 0.5-1.0 centimetres wide, make them difficult to distinguish from those of roe and muntjac. Helpful pointers though may include the fact that they adhere together less frequently than with muntjac droppings and may be less likely to be dimpled. Within a group, water deer pellets are often plumper and more uniform in size and shape than those of muntjac. Also piles ranging in number from single pellets to a hundred or more can litter rides marking territory boundaries in the winter rut. Some similar marking is also done within territories. Buck water deer make scrapes, in which they urinate and defecate to mark their territories, but these can be confused with those made by muntjac.

In soft mud or snow, the slot measures about 4-5 centimetres in length by 3-4 centimetres in width, which is intermediate in size between the slots of muntjac and roe deer. Marks of dew claws can be seen in deep snow or when running (unlike muntjac) and the inner side of each cleave is straighter than for either of the other species. The hind footprints fall more or less precisely on top of the fore prints when walking. The distance between pairs of left side or right side prints is 60-75 centimetres (most usually about 70 centimetres) i.e. the stride length is about 35 centimetres. This is midway between stride patterns for the other two species. Also muntjac tracks often form precise straight lines with the tracks of the right feet exactly between those of the left. As a further generalisation, water deer often walk down the length of a ride, whereas muntjac will usually walk across from cover to cover. Water deer sometimes make narrow trails, typically 10-15 centimetres wide, on rides along which

Water deer droppings

7

Water deer slots in snow on a wooden bridge.

animals may walk some distance to better feeding. They will use regular paths through reeds and other tall dense vegetation. These paths are roughly 20-25 centimetres in width and, if tunnels are formed, they are about 50 centimetres in height. Taking all of these characters into consideration, a visit to an area soon after heavy snow may readily indicate whether Chinese water deer are present and in which localities.

Other deer species fray saplings with their antlers and teeth. Water deer of course do not have antlers. Nibbling vegetation as a possible form of marking has been observed, but is unlikely to be detected by even the most sharp-eyed human observer. The same applies to thin saplings that have been drawn repeatedly between tusk and mouth by bucks marking their territories, unless the bark has been removed.

Tufts of the coarse winter coat are lost especially during fighting and can be found from October onwards through the winter, becoming most frequent in December. The hair is hollow and is about 40-55 millimetres in length; it is whitish over most of its length but then changes to a dark brown band and finally to pale brown, buff or ginger at its tip.

Senses and communication

Chinese water deer are heavily dependent on all of their senses: sight, smell and hearing. They rely to a great degree on sight to detect and evaluate danger. If disturbed they will stare intensely at the potential danger with head upright and ears pricked. This posture may be maintained for several minutes. Other water deer nearby may totally ignore this signal and continue in their own activities. Water deer also have a more relaxed scanning behaviour, which is routinely used when they have not been alarmed. Water deer mothers with young fawns are especially vigilant.

Disturbed deer staring at intruder.

Water deer are also alerted by scent. They can smell a human more than 100 metres away upwind and will move off even though they may not have seen the person. Smell is an important means of communication between the deer. Although much of water deer behaviour is geared towards avoiding one another, if deer are close they often sniff one another's heads or bodies. The sense of smell is particularly important in courtship.

Scent marking is used to define territories, and so plays a considerable role in determining how the deer use space. The scent may originate from glandular secretions or from urine and faeces. Plant stems and thin saplings are held behind the buck's tusk and with energetic head movements are rubbed past the pre-orbital gland. Vegetation is also rubbed with the forehead, although the deer have no glands there, and nibbled. Bucks mark their territories with urine and faeces, and may paw the ground with their forefeet before doing so. Small interdigital glands, which some authors have reported to be present in the forefeet, may add to the scent of the urine and faeces. However, such scrapes are relatively rarely found at Woodwalton. Bucks reduce the size of

Buck defecating

their faecal pellet groups during the rut so as to be able to increase the frequency of marking with droppings. Water deer are the only species of deer in this country with inguinal glands. If deer are handled, waxy secretions from these glands in the groins may be evident.

They are capable of emitting a range of sounds. It is very difficult to put sounds into words and most have been described differently by different authors. However, everyone agrees that the alarm call is a bark, although it is rather more of a growl than the fox-like bark of the muntjac. Water deer may bark repeatedly at a person and maybe also at one another. Certainly in many cases, the reason for a deer barking is not apparent. We have information from Woodwalton to indicate that frequency of barking by individuals increases in the summer and also in years when the population is at a low level. An increased frequency of barking has also been noticed at Whipsnade and attributed to alert behaviour by does during the season when they have fawns. Aggressive bucks will make a mechanical sound, variously described as clicking, whickering or chittering. This is most frequently heard in the rut when one buck is chasing another. How the sound is made is not known. It has been suggested that the canine teeth are used, but first winter bucks with poorly-developed canines utter the sound, as very occasionally do females. Similar mechanical noises made by other cervid species seem to involve the molar teeth, and water deer may make this sound in a similar fashion. A male pursuing a female during the rut utters a plaintive bird-like whistle or squeak. This may be used to indicate the male's intentions and also to maintain contact between the pair during the hours of darkness or in thick cover. At Woodwalton, squeaking is often heard in the dense reedbeds. Other calls heard less frequently are a soft squeak from submissive animals, a gentle whistle from a mother to her fawn, a soft scream by very young fawns and a loud screaming wail emitted by a deer in pain or distress.

Distribution and population development

The Chinese water deer has been kept in captivity in this country since the late nineteenth century. By the time of the Second World War large populations existed within the confines of Woburn Park, the proximate point of origin of all British water deer, and Whipsnade Zoo. Since then escapes have occurred, particularly from Woburn, and a few deliberate releases also. The situation as regards distribution records (see map) is that a few represent strong, extant populations but a number of others are of odd animals that have managed to escape and in some cases establish small feral populations. Some of these appear to have died out, for example in Hampshire, Northamptonshire and Shropshire, while others are of recent origin, for instance in Suffolk. The current distribution map reveals a scatter of records through East Anglia between the species strongholds in semi-natural habitat in Cambridgeshire and Norfolk.

The vast majority of water deer in this country live in and around Woburn Park, Whipsnade Zoo, Woodwalton Fen and the Norfolk Broads. It is worthwhile, therefore, discussing in detail the development of these populations. The first water deer arrived at Woburn in 1896 (they had been briefly kept at London Zoo in the 1870s). Others were imported and they bred well so that by the end of 1913, the population was 126. With the outbreak of the First World War, detailed records ceased. The population must have continued to increase as 180 died during 1935 and 1936. In 1967 nearly 300 were counted, and the current estimate is 200-300.

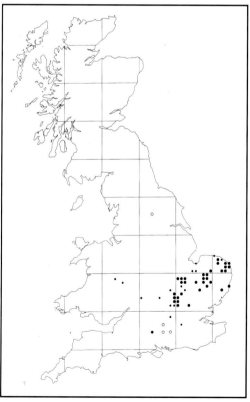

A revised distribution map for Chinese water deer on a 10 kilometre square basis: up to 1959 (open circles), 1960-1979 (small solid dots), 1980 to present (large solid dots).

11

Early morning in a wooded area of Woodwalton Fen.

The deer are said to have escaped from the park during the Second World War because Government officials working at the Abbey were lax in closing the park gates after returning from evenings out. By 1954 the deer were established within a radius of a few kilometres especially in the direction of Ampthill and Flitwick to the east and in a southerly direction towards Whipsnade, about 15 kilometres away. In 1972, 20 were culled on farmland outside the park. A survey in the early 1990s showed that most were still living within a few kilometres of the park to the south and the east, while others were more than 5 kilometres to the north. The range was limited and patchy with the total number estimated between 40 and 100.

During 1929 and 1930, 32 deer were transferred from Woburn to Whipsnade and liberated in an area of undeveloped pasture. Just three years later, the population was about 200. However, during 1933/4 about 140 died. A count in December 1936 showed the total to be 115 living at a density of about 1.7 per hectare. This is similar to the present density although water deer have since spread to other areas of the zoo so that the current number (estimated at up to 600) is higher. Deer seen occasionally outside the zoo are thought to be recent escapes or may be wanderers from Woburn.

There is a report of a small number of Chinese water deer from Woburn being released in the vicinity of Woodwalton Fen sometime around 1950. If these were the originators of the population on the reserve, they managed to be particularly secretive as it was 1962 before tracks of small deer were noticed. Although the population became well established during the 1960s it was erroneously assumed that they were muntjac (a species more or less absent from the area at that time). They were correctly identified in 1971 when a population estimate of 50-75 deer was tentatively made. We began our study in 1976 and have continued to the present day. Although we have concentrated on population change rather than absolute numbers, we estimate the population to have fluctuated between roughly 40 and 100. In the late 1970s and early 1980s there were considerable fluctuations between winters, but these became less marked during the late 1980s and early 1990s. Over the ten winters up to 1995/6, our estimates ranged between 50 and 80 animals. Water deer are regularly encountered within a 5 kilometre radius of Woodwalton Fen, both inside other reserves and on farmland. The total population in the area is probably within the range 100-200.

In the Norfolk Broads, the first record was of a buck killed on the road at Stalham in 1969. This was believed to have been a local escapee. Ten years later they were the most commonly seen species of deer in the Broads, were increasing in the Bure and Ant valleys and were along the Yare. By the mid 1990s the population was believed to number at least 300. Along some Broadland roads there are traffic warning signs, several of which appear to be specifically for water deer. Deer may be seen feeding on farmland adjacent to Broadland habitat.

Habitats

Typical habitats in China are river shores and coastal areas with reed and other tall grasses for cover, and grassland in hills and near lakes. For feeding they prefer sedge-dominated habitat where a greater diversity of food plants grow. In England, they occur in a range of habitats including grassland, arable land, reed, scrub and woodland. Arable fields used include winter wheat, oilseed rape, field beans, carrots, potatoes and, latterly and particularly, set-aside. They

Typical water deer habitat - in this case on the Bure Marshes, Norfolk Broads.

can be found in dry open habitat with virtually no cover, so neither wetness nor dense vegetation seem completely necessary. At Woodwalton, however, the adjacent arable land is utilised as part of the home range by deer living primarily inside the edge of the reserve. Few deer appear to be living totally on the farmland, although they live in such situations elsewhere in the area and outside the perimeter wall of the Woburn estate. Also at Woodwalton, territories occupied by mature bucks in prime condition have open areas of fen vegetation next to dense reed or willow carr.

A comparison has been made between sightings of Chinese water deer and muntjac in and outside Woodwalton Fen from 1987 to 1993. In the wet centre and north of the reserve, which is dominated by reed and sallow carr, about half of the total water deer sightings and about one third of the muntjac sightings were recorded. About 60% of the muntjac were recorded in the drier south where there is woodland with a bramble understorey and heathy fields; fewer than 20% of water deer were seen here. The arable land accounted for 30% of the water deer sightings but less than 10% of the muntjac encounters. Thus, relative to the muntjac, the water deer seems to prefer habitats that are both wet and unwooded. The nature, range and frequency of vocalisations supports the observation that water deer are adapted to dense cover such as reedbeds.

If cattle are introduced into such areas at Woodwalton for reserve management purposes, the deer appear to leave more or less immediately. The cattle tend to break up and flatten dense cover. There may also be some reaction to the cattle themselves as deer will return after the cattle have been moved on. The newcomers are not necessarily the original territory holders.

Feeding and food

At least during daytime, water deer spend about half of their time feeding. Feeding occurs in bouts of about 20 minutes punctuated by periods of resting and ruminating. Ruminating is regurgitating and chewing partly-digested food, prior to it being further digested in the various compartments of the stomach. Water deer also feed at night, although detailed time budgets have yet to be determined for the hours of darkness. Peaks in feeding activity occur in the early morning and in the evening. At Woodwalton, deer are most active just after sunset.

Water deer either bite off vegetation from a plant or grasp it between their lower incisors and their upper dental pad and tear it away. Small species of deer tend to be either concentrate selectors or mixed feeders. They have fairly simple stomachs that are able to digest foods low in fibre, but whose cells are rich in soluble nutrients. Larger species of deer, which are bulk and roughage feeders, have more complex stomachs able to break down the cellulose in plant cell walls. The water deer has been classified on the basis of gut anatomy as being

First winter deer grazing.

a concentrate selector, but is not such an extreme example as the muntjac. Studies on its food do not, however, completely support this supposition as grasses and similar species contribute a considerable proportion of its diet.

Examination of rumen contents at Whipsnade in spring of 1994 revealed that 71% of plant fragments were grasses, sedges and rushes, 24% were herbs and 4% were woody plants. However, the situation at Whipsnade is such that herbs are relatively restricted in diversity and availability and woody browse is very limited, in part because larger animals have produced a browse line too high for water deer to reach. Forage is considered to be suboptimal for water deer throughout the year at Whipsnade on the basis of stomach anatomy and diet. This is presumably why they are significantly smaller than at Woodwalton or in China. In a study in China where deer were presented with a range of plant species, 24% of the species taken were grasses and sedges, 59% were herbs and 17% were woody species. Mainly leaves were eaten. In another Chinese study of rumen contents, 93% of fragments were herbs; while in a third study 96% of rumens contained the ericaceous species *Vaccinium bracteatum*. Rumens were examined for deer found dead in Cambridgeshire during the winter and spring. There was considerable variation between animals, but the overall ratio of fragments was 66:34 for graze:browse species. This comparatively high figure for browsed fragments was surprising in view of the fact that water deer are only very rarely recorded browsing in the wild in this country. The deer evidently browse regularly when hidden by scrub and other cover. By far the most important browse species is bramble, which is particularly essential at times of snow cover.

In China, water deer take a variety of crops such as soyabeans, peanuts and sweet potatoes. In this country they feed on fields of carrots (particularly the green tops), winter wheat and potatoes left after harvest. However, when seen on or beside arable land, they are usually taking weeds such as chickweed rather than the crop plants. In captivity they will eat root vegetables, but there are reports that they will not eat hay, even when starving.

In summary the water deer is a selective feeder on a range of grasses, sedges and herbs with some woody species being taken.

Social behaviour

Apart from during mating, the behaviour of a buck water deer is largely aimed at maximising the distance between himself and other water deer. Although does are much less aggressive, water deer tend to be solitary animals. Surveys of group size showed that most sightings were of single deer: e.g. China, 85% in the breeding season and 55% in the rut; Woodwalton, 85% throughout the year. Even in the crowded environment of Whipsnade, 34% of observations were of single animals and 32% of pairs through the year. At Woodwalton the tendency to be solitary increases as the level of the population decreases. In the wild, group size rarely, if ever, reaches ten. Females may form loose associations with one another outside the fawning period, but if alarmed are likely to disperse in totally different directions.

Much of the behaviour shown by bucks in particular is aggressive in nature. Most encounters between males begin with one deer approaching in a ritualised, aggressive manner with stiff gait. Rival bucks might then indulge in parallel-walking, where both adopt the aggressive posture but walk more or less parallel to one another and 10-20 metres apart. Hostilities might then develop into a chase with the following male making the clicking noise. If both males decline to run away, a fight is likely to result. The bucks dance around one another trying to land blows with their canines. Many bucks have scars and ragged ears which testify to the frequency and intensity of fighting. Another indicator of the amount of fighting during the rut is the frequent tufts of hair that have been lost to canine blows.

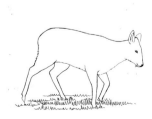

Bucks parallel-walking.

Play behaviour has been observed in all sex and age categories although fawns aged 1-2 months are most active at play. Such behaviour might involve running, head-shaking, jumping and twisting. In some cases single individuals play, in others, several play close together. We have occasionally seen single deer at Woodwalton bucking and prancing and shaking their heads as if to rid themselves of parasites in the ears! This may be a form of play.

Ranging and territory

A territory is an area to which a deer has a spatial bond and which it will defend. A home range is the area occupied by an individual during its normal activities. Unlike territories, home ranges may show considerable overlap.

In a study at Whipsnade, average annual home range size was 21 hectares: 12 hectares for older males (older than two years), but about 25 hectares for older females and for second year deer. As regards seasonal home ranges (measured during four three-month periods through the year), these were largest for older females (about 10 hectares) and second year deer (about 15 hectares) during May-July, whereas for older males, seasonal range size was less than 5 hectares throughout the year. Of the older males, some were territorial and some were not. Annual range size of the territory holders was only two hectares and their seasonal range averaged one hectare. About 30% of the bucks retained their territorial hold throughout the 27 months of the study. It was also suggested that at least one third of bucks in their second year or older were unable to hold territories. Our limited observations at Woodwalton on five identifiable deer during the mid winter rut gave ranges varying from 5 to 15 hectares.

In one population in China, mean seasonal home ranges were found to vary between 18 and 46 hectares depending on season and methodology. In a second study, however, bucks followed does to better feeding grounds and set up small territories of about half a hectare clustered together but with no overlap. Does were present at a density of 1.6 per hectare. The conclusion must be that while the bucks try to establish and retain territories, their spatial arrangement is flexible and will vary according to local conditions.

In contrast to bucks, does are generally less aggressive and do not hold territories during the rut. However, there is some evidence for them being territorial before and after giving birth. This has been recorded

Does sometimes fight.

17

amongst captive animals, while at Woodwalton there is a second phase of aggression from March to May when chases involving two does can be observed. At Whipsnade average size of home range for fawns was about 2 hectares during their first three months of life, then increased steadily to about 10 hectares by the winter months.

Breeding

Chinese water deer rut annually. Indications that the rut is approaching, for instance observations of squeaking bucks following does, may occur as early as October. However, the main rutting months are November and December, with activity continuing into January. Males will attempt to associate with does in their territories with increasing intensity as oestrus approaches. The oestrous state of the females is regularly checked. Bucks approach does with their necks below the horizontal and with rotating movements of the head producing ear slapping. At Whipsnade, bucks have been noted as attempting to retain females within their territories by circling them.

In one Chinese study, rutting males were found to establish their small territories in areas where females clustered. At Whipsnade, female distribution may be more clumped than at other times of year and males whose territories are based in such localities may benefit. At Woodwalton, deer seem to be fairly evenly spaced through the reserve throughout the year. Nevertheless certain hot spots for mating activity can be identified. Presumably any rutting buck holding a territory that contains no females will attempt to rectify the situation by modifying the territory or moving completely. Males can become territory holders either by ousting an existing holder or by establishing themselves between territories and then gradually increasing their patches.

During oestrus, a male will court and repeatedly mount a doe. Copulation takes a few seconds only - we have never seen it at Woodwalton. Recorded matings elsewhere have occurred in December and January. The large majority of matings occur with the male in his own territory. Occasionally a male may mate with more than one female, the mating system being polygynous. Does in their first breeding season may conceive and in some populations their conception rate is not significantly different to that of older animals. Elsewhere, many females may not breed until their second winter.

Young bucks also reach sexual maturity in their first winter but in situations where the competition is fierce they may show courtship behaviour but not mate successfully. At Whipsnade many males do not become territory holders until after their second rut; some males never seem to acquire

Attentive buck pursuing a doe.

Doe giving birth accompanied by newly-born fawns.

territories. In the less crowded arena at Woodwalton some territories during the rut are occupied by first year bucks. This does not mean, however, that they necessarily mate successfully.

The water deer is the most prolific species of deer. As many as seven foetuses have been recorded in a single doe in China, but four seems to be the most recorded in this country. If three or more ova are involved in a single ovulation, implantation rate is reduced. Internal examination of dead females during the early months of the year reveals an increasing proportion of pregnant animals up until the early spring. For example in a Chinese study, frequency of pregnancy increased from 29% in February to 86% in March.

Numbers of foetuses and litter sizes at birth have been recorded by several authors, with the mean numbers invariably being in the range 2-3. Litter sizes of twins and triplets are probably most common. The fecundity of first year does that breed successfully is comparable to that of older deer. Estimates of gestation length vary between 165 and 210 days. Sex ratio of foetuses is roughly unity. The same seems to apply to the sex ratio of fawns although there have been occasional reports of a sex imbalance in small captive populations.

May and June are the main months for parturition, but some births are outside this period. Does do not seem to select particular microhabitats for giving birth. At Whipsnade, birth sites include open grass fields, nettle beds and copses. When we have found fawns at Woodwalton, they have been in the open fen fields. Newborn fawns are able to stand after about one hour and have been

19

Well grown fawns.

recorded as moving more than 100 metres during their first day of life. At birth most fawns weigh 0.6-1.0 kilograms. Initial weight gain is approximately 0.1 kilogram per day.

Fawns spend most of their early life lying concealed in vegetation. In most cases they hide singly but occasionally two or three may be found together. Fawns are visited by their mothers a few times each day for bouts of suckling and grooming. After periods of care, fawns move away to select another hiding place. Towards the end of their first month, fawns spend less time lying out; but when they do, they may tend to select more exposed situations, for example in shorter grass. Vegetation is nibbled from a few days of age. Young are weaned at about three months although length of suckling bouts declines well before this time. They can be seen associating with other fawns that are not necessarily siblings.

At Woodwalton in September and October, fawns are often seen on the adjacent arable land, either singly or in small groups. These may be young deer that are about to disperse away from the reserve, probably having been driven out of their natal ranges.

Dispersal and movement

With water deer does able to give birth to several young at a time, a population is always likely to produce surplus young. These will probably be driven away and will need to find somewhere to live. Observations of deer in suboptimal habitat or of road casualties well away from known populations may be of dispersing animals. Roads are not an insurmountable barrier, however, as they have evidently crossed the M1 motorway and the main trunk road, the A5, when dispersing away from Woburn. Inland waters are unlikely to be any barrier as they are known to swim several kilometres between islands in China. There are anecdotal reports of individual water deer travelling considerable distances. For instance, one seen near Ripon in Yorkshire in 1952 was assumed to have escaped earlier that year from near Harrogate, 15 kilometres away.

But are they really such good colonisers? The first record from Woodwalton Fen was in 1962 and by the late 1960s there was a well established population. However, it was 1976 before there was a definite record from Monks Wood which is only 5 kilometres to the south-west of Woodwalton Fen. The species was first seen in 1977 in Holme Fen, about 5 kilometres to the north-west, although signs had been noted in the mid 1970s. These dates are probably 5-10 years after there was significant pressure on deer to disperse away from Woodwalton, so this evidence suggests a dispersal rate of 1 kilometre per annum or less. This is comparable to the recorded dispersal rate of muntjac.

In addition to natural dispersal, populations may need to respond to various events by moving. In China, some deer are forced by seasonal flooding to forsake low lying grassy deltas for hill country several kilometres away. This is similar, although on a grander scale, to the situation in Woodwalton Fen. Here, flooding in the reserve (which serves as a water storage area at time of high precipitation) can force deer to move temporarily to the drier south of the reserve, to the flood-banks and to the farmland. At Wheatfen Broad in Norfolk, where the water system is tidal, deer are forced onto higher ground at high tides. There are also reports from China and from Whipsnade of seasonal movements to better grazing. At Woodwalton, foraging on the adjacent arable land reaches a peak in the early months of the year when food is probably least available within the reserve.

Mortality, disease and parasites

Mortality of fawns can be considerable. A study in one area at Woburn in the 1970s indicated 25% mortality up to three days of age mainly due to stillbirths and hyperthermia in an open environment. In another captive population, the mortality rate was 40% during the first four weeks of life, attributed to stillbirths and exposure. Neither of these studies regarded predation as being important. However, in a study of fawn mortality at Whipsnade in 1993, fox

Prolonged snow cover may cause mortality.

predation was thought to be the principal factor; attacks by carrion crows were also witnessed. At Woodwalton, we have estimated the mean number of young present in winter to be 0.5 per adult female, with a range of 0 to 1.4. Set against a likely birth rate of two fawns per female, this indicates that overall, about three quarters of the fawns either die or are forced out of the reserve before their first winter.

Rate of loss (i.e. including emigration) for adult deer at Woodwalton increases to about 40% when severe winter weather with prolonged snow cover or flooding forces deer to vacate their normal ranges. Although our worst weather should be within the extremes the species faces in China, especially the monsoon rains, problems have also been noted during snow cover in, for instance, the Broads, Whipsnade and Woburn. During the long severe winter of 1946/7 it was feared that virtually the whole population at Woburn might die. Their refusal to eat hay can hamper attempts to reduce the death rate amongst captive stock. When we have undertaken postmortem examinations of winter casualties there was often no obvious cause of death. Dead deer can be in good condition with digestible material in their stomachs. A combination of wet and cold weather appears most damaging. Amongst these winter casualties, dead bucks usually outnumber does.

Adults may also be killed in a variety of other ways. Death on the roads has provided us with many records, sometimes in places where the species had not been suspected. Adult water deer are regularly shot and make good eating. In

China the number hunted per annum is believed to be roughly equivalent to the mid-winter population. Even allowing for the prolific nature of the species, this is unlikely to be sustainable. In one study in China up to 70% of the second year age class were killed. Amongst other things, this illustrates how easy water deer are to shoot. They often frequent open areas and when grazing present a static or slow moving target. Both here and in China, native predators of adult deer are absent. However, dogs may catch and kill deer; at Woburn, incidents have been described in which the deer succumbed without even running away.

Death due to fighting between bucks is a rare event, but injuries commonly result. In a study at Whipsnade, more than 90% of injuries were attributed to fighting. These included damaged eyes, ripped ears, scars up to 30 centimetres long and limping. Some of these injuries may reduce life expectancy. At Woodwalton we have noticed a number of crippled, limping animals. Many of these appeared to have been injured, but others may have had diseased joints or other defects. When water deer have been caught for scientific purposes, deaths have sometimes been noted which have been blamed on hyperthermia or capture myopathy. The physiological and biochemical processes involved in the second condition remain to be confirmed, but metabolic acidosis and damage to muscle fibre cells are known to occur.

A mature buck's tusks are impressive weapons.

Chinese water deer living in parks at high densities have greater numbers of ticks (*Ixodes* spp), deer flies (*Lipoptaena* spp) and lice than feral deer. Lice on does are found to be concentrated in areas such as the face, groin and mammary gland from where they can readily transfer to fawns. The epidemic which killed 140 deer at Whipsnade in 1933/4 was described as 'enteritis', the grazing of frozen pasture perhaps being implicated. Demodectic mange has also been reported from Whipsnade.

Population density and dynamics

Estimates of density depend to some extent on how the area occupied is calculated: whether only a figure for the core area is taken or whether extra land used seasonally is taken into account or whether unused land within the range is discounted. In China estimates of population density vary between 3 and 90 deer per square kilometre, with most being towards the low end of the range. Probably the two most natural occupied areas in England are Woodwalton Fen and the Norfolk Broads. At Woodwalton, based on the area of the reserve, density is estimated at 19-48 per square kilometre. However, the true figure may be only about half this range, as this does not take into account foraging onto the farmland. For the Broads, using figures of at least 300 deer and an available area of suitable habitat of 30 square kilometres or more yields an estimate of roughly 10 per square kilometre. In some areas of Broadland, such as on the marshes to the north of Woodbastwick, the density of signs is comparable to that at Woodwalton. These British estimates are within the range for China whereas, at Whipsnade, recent estimates have included 140 per square kilometre for the whole zoo and 240 per square kilometre for the main study area. These figures are higher than from elsewhere and it is not surprising to find that the deer are significantly smaller. A crude estimate for the farmland area outside the park at Woburn is <2 per square kilometre. This is lower than other estimates probably indicating the suboptimal nature of the habitat.

Sex ratios for the different age classes have not been found to depart significantly from parity. Deer are capable of breeding in their first

Recruitment level in winter can be calculated from proportions of deer seen with or without tusks.

24

winter and a study at Whipsnade in 1937 indicated that if there was no mortality or emigration, the population could, in theory, double in a year. When animals were shot in that study, 38% were first year animals. Our own observations of live deer at Whipsnade in December 1979 suggested 27% first year deer. Of 117 tagged animals in June 1994, 41% were one year olds, the rest being older. In a population in China where there is much shooting, 48% of those shot were first year deer, 37% second year and 15% older; expectation of further life for the survivors was only about one year.

We calculate recruitment to the winter population on the basis of the proportions of sightings of animals with and without tusks, assuming equal numbers of males and females and an equal chance of seeing the different age/sex classes. The annual level of recruitment at Woodwalton has varied from 0 to 42% over the last two decades, with an average of 20% - rather lower than at Whipsnade and much lower than in the Chinese study. Thus, during a year when the population remains stable, an average recruitment of 20% will be balanced by a loss of adults of 20%. Over the years the winter population has varied by little more than two fold, and there is evidence of density dependence. It is possible that winter losses of adults are fairly quickly compensated for by production of young, with surplus animals being forced out of the reserve each autumn. Over the ten years up to 1995/6 when the population was particularly stable, mean recruitment was 17% (range 0-29%) and mean loss of adults 17% (range 4-30%).

Chinese water deer also now have to contend with the presence of muntjac, which is becoming established over much of lowland England. At Woodwalton Fen, muntjac began to colonise in 1980. In the drier south of the reserve where muntjac are evidently more at home, water deer sightings have declined to about half their former level. The situation now seems to have reached equilibrium with populations of both species having stabilised. In the reedbeds and willow carr in the centre and north, muntjac have been slower to colonise and water deer have not declined. The nature of the competition in the south is unknown. However, bramble and other shrubs in the south show marked browse-lines in the winter and it is possible that amount of browse at least may be limiting. In Holme Fen, which is primarily birch woodland with a bramble and bracken understorey, water deer appeared to arrive a few years before muntjac. Over the last ten years, however, sightings of muntjac have increased significantly while sightings of water deer have declined. In Monks Wood, a large wood dominated by ash, muntjac began to colonise in about 1970 and from 1985 have formed the densest population documented in this country (at least 100 per square kilometre). Water deer were first recorded in 1976. The wood is probably not particularly suitable for them and water deer have never been very numerous. Sightings tend to be centred on the open, part-mown fields within the wood and also areas of failed coppice. Sightings declined significantly from the mid 1980s to the mid 1990s, associated with the very high population of muntjac. In both Holme Fen and Monks Wood, bramble is very heavily defoliated in winter. Similar changes in deer numbers have been noted among island populations in China where Reeves' muntjac occurs. Competition in Britain is likely to be worse for the water deer in dry scrub or woodland habitats and less serious in wet, grassy or open situations.

Management and conservation

Outside parks in this country, water deer density is less than 50 per square kilometre. Aggregations of more than three or four are rare. They are small deer with a dry matter requirement of about half a kilogram per day. Although they will browse, they tend to take grasses, sedges and herbaceous species of plant. They are said not to harm young plantations. Situations where they may come into conflict with land managers will be rarely encountered but could include farm crops and some nature reserves if they focus on flora of conservation importance. In China they have until recently been perceived to be agricultural pests and were shot in large numbers; the situation has changed because of their scarcity and legal status. They are shot on farmland in this country, for instance outside both Woburn Park and Woodwalton Fen, but some is sport shooting. On farmland adjacent to Woodwalton Fen, no damage has been noticed except on carrot fields where it has been minimal. They will sometimes feed on winter wheat, however, and the current trend towards winter drilling rather than spring drilling could lead to some local problems being

The water deer seems not to be a serious pest but further feeding studies are needed.

perceived. Although most farmers are doubtless not pleased to see deer grazing on their crops, the impact of this species on agricultural interests should be slight.

While the denser feral populations have some potential to affect native flora, there are few reported examples. In Woodwalton Fen, grazing, blamed on the deer, has occurred on a proportion of great water docks, the food plant of the caterpillar of the introduced large copper butterfly. However, unless specific studies are made either on the diet of the species or on grazing losses of possible food plants, impacts may not be readily apparent. In the Bure Marshes National Nature Reserve in the Norfolk Broads, regrowth on alder coppice is not touched, but deer generally find alder unpalatable; some browsing on regrowth of ash and willow is apparent. If water deer do need to be kept out of sensitive areas, muntjac fencing will probably suffice. This should be 1.5 metres in height and have a mesh size not exceeding 75 millimetres.

As water deer grow and mature rapidly, does have several fawns at a time and the venison is highly acceptable, the species has been suggested for livestock farming. However, enclosures need to be at least one hectare in size with plenty of refuges in which deer can hide, and there is the problem of territoriality and fighting. We are not aware of anyone farming them successfully.

Although still rare here, the English population of water deer may represent about 10% of the world's total of the Chinese subspecies. It is recognised, both in China and internationally, as being in need of protection. Fortunately, most of our wild water deer are based in Sites of Special Scientific Interest, which means the sites, if not necessarily the deer, are safeguarded. The same is likely to apply in the future if the species continues to colonise reedbeds. Nevertheless, further conservation measures should be considered for this important and interesting addition to our fauna. At the very least, its presence in a reserve should be viewed positively by conservation managers.

Legal status

The Chinese water deer was categorised as 'rare' on the IUCN Red List of 1990 and 'vulnerable' in 1994. On the Red List in 1996, concern for the Chinese subspecies amended its classification to "lower risk, near threatened", whereas the status of the Korean subspecies was "data deficient". The Chinese subspecies is a protected animal in its native land. In Britain, it is covered by the same general legislation as the muntjac. It is illegal to use a rifle with a calibre of less than 0.240 or with a muzzle energy of less than 1700 foot pounds. Curiously, there is no close season for water deer despite the fact that they are clearly seasonal breeders.

The future in this country

Under this heading one can ask a series of questions:

- Is the water deer under-recorded, people often mistaking it for the muntjac?
- Why has it colonised England much less well than the muntjac?
- Is it currently increasing and will it increase in the future?

None of these questions is easy to answer. Undoubtedly some misidentification has occurred and still occurs, but the public is becoming better informed. Hopefully this booklet will help further.

We now know that the muntjac owes much of its colonisation of lowland England to accidental and deliberate releases by man. It is not the great natural coloniser it was once thought to be - and neither is the water deer. The water deer has been at a disadvantage in this respect because escapes/releases have occurred from far fewer foci.

But surely it could have done better? Climate seems unlikely to be a problem and the same applies to barriers such as rivers and roads. Natural predators, at least on adults, are not a problem. However, we suspect that shooting may have nipped in the bud a number of attempts at colonisation. Water deer have primarily been trying to establish themselves in East Anglia which is a rural and heavily shot-over area. Water deer present an attractive and easy target in

Multiple births should aid its colonisation of this country.

the wide open spaces of the region, through which they must disperse. Further, if their preferred habitat is wet reedbed and thick grassland, this is in fairly short supply. More marginal habitat, such as arable land, is plentiful but water deer appear not to build up to high densities there. Wood and scrub may also be marginal habitats and are situations where they can come into competition with muntjac - and seem to come out second best.

In time, Chinese water deer will presumably colonise other reedbeds in the east of the country. They have now got a toe-hold at Minsmere in east Suffolk and are eventually likely to establish populations at sites in East Anglia such as Wicken Fen (where a single animal was recorded in 1982) and Chippenham Fen (where they will have competition from a sizeable population of roe deer). Once established in each of these areas, surplus animals are likely to spill out into suboptimal habitats, much as they have around Woodwalton Fen. Water deer will benefit from the creation of new reedbeds, such as those promoting conservation of the bittern. They are also appreciating agricultural set-aside and will benefit in the future from whatever low intensity farming system follows it. Such habitats present a better alternative to arable crops, both for living in and dispersing through.

We suggest that although individual deer may disperse considerable distances, their rate of natural colonisation is unlikely to be substantially greater than one kilometre per year in terms of establishment. In order to colonise other parts of the country, therefore, they are dependent on escaping from collections or being released in other regions. There are captive water deer in at least ten locations countrywide, and the potential exists to colonise other regions. Although some populations have proved to be transitory, the stability of the population at Woodwalton, for instance, demonstrates they can thrive under

Often an animal of open spaces, it is relatively easy to shoot.

29

British conditions. So water deer are here to stay even if their future spread in terms of both numbers and range may be rather slow. Once established in a locality, if they do not come into conflict with other interests, they should be regarded and conserved as an interesting and valuable addition to our fauna.

Research that would aid our understanding of the species includes provision of information on diet in the wild (including confirmation that they do not significantly damage young trees or coppice regrowth), on densities and body condition of deer in different habitats (to help confirm exactly where they do well) and on dispersal and use of space. As regards the last item, a programme of tagging fawns in a site such as Woodwalton would be of great interest.

The situation in China

There are written records of water deer in China dating back to the third century BC. During historic times it has been considered an abundant animal over much of the country. Swinhoe was the first person to describe the Chinese water deer to the western world. That was in 1870 when he considered it to occur in large numbers on the riverine islands of the Yangtze. One hundred years later, standard reference books on deer indicated a range over much of north east China connecting up with the range of the Korean subspecies. The Chinese subspecies was still being described as abundant within its range. We have to confess repeating such complacent statements in previous accounts that we have written. In reality, both the range and the number of animals have declined drastically over the last half century, largely as a result of loss of habitat and poaching. The remaining populations have become isolated and even more vulnerable to these threats. Estimates of the total population in China are as low as 10,000 animals. Distribution is now restricted to the shores of the lower reaches of the Yangtze River and nearby lake areas, coastal areas of Jiangsu Province and the Zhoushan Islands in Zhejiang Province. Its distribution is now best described as being limited to only parts of eastern China.

Currently it is in the Class Two category of protected animals in China. This should mean that permission is needed from the wildlife authorities before one is caught or killed. Amazingly because of its unique population dynamics, the total estimated in the early 1990s to be killed by hunters each year was the same as the total population, 10,000! Many neonates are taken for the colostrum in their stomachs, which is a prized medicine in China. Many deer are hunted for the pot and until recently others were killed because they were believed to be pests to crops. Utilising the deer as food is evidently in marked contrast to Swinhoe's time when he remarked on the 'extraordinary dislike' of the locals for water deer venison. At that time deer were shot in numbers by Europeans and also by locals for the European market.

The solutions to problems in China seem to be better protection against hunting where the species occurs, the provision of corridors between isolated populations and education of the local people. Without such provisions the time may come when more of the Chinese subspecies live in England than China, and English stock might one day have to be reintroduced back to its native range.

Scene outside a Chinese village.

Further reading

The Chinese water deer remains the least known of the species of deer covered by booklets in this series. While there is no other recent broad account of the Chinese water deer in this country there are a number of general books that are well worth consulting on this and other species:

Chaplin, R. E. 1977. *Deer.* Poole: Blandford Press. A general text, but with much first hand observation of Chinese water deer.

Corbet, G. B & Harris, S. 1991. *The handbook of British mammals,* 3rd edition. Oxford: Blackwell Scientific Publications. Has sections detailing basic information on all of the British mammals.

Harris, S., Morris, P., Wray, S. & Yalden, D. 1995. *A review of British mammals: population estimates and conservation status of British mammals other than cetaceans.* Peterborough: JNCC. An up-to-date account of our mammalian resource.

Putman, R. 1988. *The natural history of deer.* London: Christopher Helm. How the biology of water deer relates to that of other species.

Sheng, H. 1992. *The deer in China.* Shanghai: East China Normal University. A general text about Chinese deer including sections on water deer and conservation.

Useful addresses

The British Deer Society, Burgate Manor, Fordingbridge, Hampshire SP6 1EF. Telephone 01425 655434; Fax 01425 655433.

The Mammal Society, 15 Cloisters Business Centre, 8 Battersea Park Road, London SW8 4BG. Telephone 0171 498 4358.

Acknowledgements

First we must thank the field staff and specialists of the Nature Conservancy Council and English Nature for their help and support since 1976 in our study at Woodwalton Fen. Most of the information from Whipsnade has been gleaned from the postgraduate studies of Stefan Stadler and Endi Zhang. We are also grateful to Endi Zhang for keeping us up-to-date with research on the species in China. Henry Arnold of the Institute of Terrestrial Ecology has kindly revised the distribution map for this publication. Michael Clark provided a number of the slides. Sarah Wroot did the drawings, most of which are from photographs by Stefan Stadler and Endi Zhang. Norma Chapman, Tony Mitchell-Jones and Endi Zhang kindly commented on a draft of the manuscript.